Front Cover FIRST DAY OF THE NEW SEASON

Rink 8   *"Well I'm not bowling the first wood"*
Rink 7   *"Oh dear, cots in the road again"*
Rink 6   *"OK I'm holding the wood right, now what?"*
Rink 5   *"A perfect delivery, oops forgot the wood"*

A HILARIOUS 'BEGINNERS GUIDE' TO BOWLING

"The 500kg, 28ft monster plunged to the ground denuding all the trees of their leafy foliage within a ten-metre radius."

"Cries of 'I KNOW WHERE YOUR WIFE WAS LAST NIGHT', as the lead is about to bowl, is a keen favourite."

"As fifty woods collide, the cot is usually re-located to the other side of the village and a cloud of chalk dust rises like a Saharan sandstorm."

"Well done partner that's a good length!"

"The ensuing massacre of the local worm population may be noted and recorded by the watching Greenpeace official."

"There's more wood in front of the cot then there is in a B & Q timber yard."

"You're supposed to be drawing to the little white thing, not killing wildlife in the hedgerow, your last wood got a speeding ticket!!"

A DONATION FROM EVERY BOOK SALE WILL BE MADE TO THE ENGLISH BOWLING ASSOCIATION TO PROMOTE THE FUTURE OF THE SPORT AND COACH NEW BOWLERS

ACKNOWLEDGMENTS

The ancient and gentlemanly sport of bowls, steeped in history and folklore, now gains a new perspective as a local club bowler turns the game on its head in an amusing, often hilarious satire of this popular pastime.

From Rules to Competitions, Commentary to Compendium the author explores the innermost 'language' of the game in a refreshing and light-hearted look.

This 'factually' based interspersion of trivia with tales, summaries, and short stories in an easy to understand dialogue approaches the ancient sport in a truly modern way.

Its characterisations strike a key as this popular game continues to develop through all ages. Members old and new are sure to enjoy this first publication from a budding author and bowler.

All characters, places, and definitions within this book are fictional

All bowling terms and shots are real, genuine, identifiable, and recognised names within bowling.

All commentary is, as heard on and off the green, with the authors own definition.

The author would like to express his thanks to all the members of Sole Bay Bowls Club for their competitiveness and friendship during the season(s) past.

In particular, thank you to John Ansdell for providing photographs which we have proceeded to 'mutilate' and caricature.

Thank you to David Ladd who has provided some inspired moments of bowling in friendly competitions through the year.

Thanks to Roy Taylor a lifetime friend, one of the few people I know who can bowl well, tell a good joke, and still buys the coffee after losing.

Also to Cliff Adams who was unable to keep a straight face whilst 'volunteering' to read some 'inspired' phrases out at the clubs annual awards presentation.

A special thanks to Cliff Howard of the English Bowling Association who has tirelessly assisted in bringing this project to fruition.

To Tony Allcock for offering his vital support and to all bowlers who have been my inspiration.

And finally, a large thank you to my hard working and understanding partner Denise who has inspired and supported me wholeheartedly through this bowling adventure.

THE BOWLING CLUB

Paul Hammond
First Edition

Jenner Publications
Leiston

Limited First Edition

Published by:

Jenner Publications
Unit 2c
Eastlands Road Ind. Est.
Leiston, Suffolk IP16 4LL
enquiries@jennerpublications.net
www.jennerpublications.net

Printed by:

Leiston Press
Unit 1B
Masterlord Ind. Est.
Leiston, Suffolk IP16 4JD

ISBN Number 0-9546633-0-6

Distributed by Jenner Publications
First Published April 2004

JENNER PUBLICATIONS
Inspiration from Suffolk

INTRODUCTION

In the Sleepy Countryside of Suffolk, amid the ancient willows and thatched cottages of peaceful hamlets lies the small village of Lower South-burgh.

Adorned by picturesque duck pond, heraldic sign, carefully trimmed hedgerows and freshly swept pathways, there stands a tired wooden building with an objective lean (depending on the wind direction).

Nearby, a small pile of bricks under an old tarpaulin promises possibilities of potential new construction, as they have done for many a year.

Weathered timber seats stand proudly in front of a more robust timber framework. This is the members 'clubhouse', a Victorian structure whose majestic windows offer, when cleaned, a splendid panoramic inspection of the on-goings outside.

The clubhouse overlooks a magnificent lawn, rectangular in shape, which on closer inspection proves to have a formidable ditch and bank much like a medieval castle but with numbers and markers attached to its structure.

The grass is short, mostly, with some threadbare patches towards its edges, but its carefully manicured form can leave the visitor in no doubt that this is indeed the village bowling green.

It is the 1st of May, with a hint of summer in the air as the warm sun rises over the trees. Birds begin to sing, butterflies flutter and the distant 'putt-putt' of a small two-stroke engine disturbs the distant tranquil calm.

It is the warming motor of the clubs ancient lawnmower emerging from a ramshackle recently stained shed at the edge of the green announcing to all that it is indeed the first day of the new bowling season.

The Rev. Percival 'Percy' Peabody, proudly prepares for the new day ahead, his first in the honorary position as 'assistant green keeper', and more importantly his first solo venture in 'green preparation'.

So welcome then to the new day, the first day of another season with the members and wives of **The Bowling Club**.

CONTENTS

Available 2005
THE BOWLING CLUBS FIRST DAY

MEET THE TEAM

PRESIDENT
The Rt. Hon. Ronald "SQUIFFY" Regis
Former RAF Squadron Commander

CHAIRMAN AND PAST PRESIDENT
Bernard 'BATTY' Bartrum
Dubious DIY Plumber, 'ladies' man, very inquisitive

VICE CHAIRMAN
Douglas Dolittle MBE
Retired Surgeon, posh, wealthy suburbanite

HON SECRETARY
Charles 'CHARLIE' Chesterford
Former cricketer, couldn't play, nothing's changed!

HON TREASURER
Reginald Trimley Esq.
Accountant, shortsighted, easily distracted

HON. COMPETITION SECRETARY
Jack 'BIG JIM' Tuttle
Larger than life, eats for England, drinks like a fish

HON. TOURING TEAM SECRETARY
Position vacant
Life beyond Suffolk has never been discovered

CAPTAIN
Rt. Hon. Clifford James Johnson
Councillor, well-respected, good bowler, 'Jack the Lad'

VICE CAPTAIN
Derek Dunstable
Quick tempered, average bowler, fiery combination

LADIES CAPTAIN
Doris 'POSH' Dolittle
Impoverished socialite, vegan, questionable morals

GREEN KEEPER
Patrick 'POSTIE' Albright
Retired postman, keen, serious, a 'by the book' player

Assistant GREEN KEEPER
Rev Percival 'PERCY' Peabody
Very helpful, eager, accident prone, can't bowl

CLUB CHAMPION
Dennis 'STICKY' Ditherford
Ornithologist, excellent bowler, tall but slightly built

SELECTION COMMITTEE
Rt. Hon. Clifford James Johnson
Derek Dunstable
James 'BIG JIM' Tuttle

UMPIRE
Eric 'CHALKIE' Tunstall
Retired pilot, enjoys life, plays a jolly good game

THE BEGINNER
Bertie Tattleford
Sales rep, explosive, cocky, can bowl well at times

COACH
Tony 'TRIGGER' Havershall
Council worker, serious player, but not too 'clever'

David Dimpley
Retired, humorous, easy going, outstanding bowler

Colin Spindleforth
Thirty-something family man with mid-life crisis

Russell Cobblethwaite SNR
Most senior member, 70 years a bowler, still sharp

Frenchie 'WIDE BOY' Phillips
A 'ladies' man with a silver tongue also bowls well

James 'SCOTTIE' Mc Carver
Talks a good game, steady player, easily distracted

Paul Jenner Esq.
New kid on the block, determined and competitive

Pauline Jenner
'Wannabe' mum, highly ambitious, somewhat blunt

Timothy 'TINY' Dolittle
Little Timmy, 13, Vice-Chairman's son, eager to learn

Johnny Jackson
Clubs hot new signing and aspiring County player

Molly Coddle (Miss)
Long-suffering tea lady, single, pursued constantly

Phillipa Spindleforth
Working class councillor aspiring to be somewhat 'posh'

THE BOWLING CLUB CONSTITUTION

TITLE
Usually indicative of the full title of the club, ours for example is "The fellowship of the guild of Lower South-borough EBA Professional Bowlers Association (Eastern Region) twinned with South-Borough City, State of Kansas, USA, affiliated to His Royal Majesty Don Sebastian Miguel of the Southern Isles.

OBJECTS
Primarily the purpose of the formation of the club inasmuch to promote, improve and indulge in the gentlemanly sport of Bowling; notwithstanding the monthly rotation of the club bar stock and contents.
The registration form incorrectly completed by our shortsighted secretary now includes an inventory of thirty assorted cups and saucers, two teapots and an old fridge.

MEMBERSHIP
You will need to provide a year's previous accounts, a bank statement, passport, driving licence, three references, a personalised letter of recommendation and an introduction from an established member of the club.

That's just to get you the opportunity to talk to the secretary!!

FEES AND SUBSCRIPTIONS
All members are required to pay Registration fees, as well as Rink fees, Tea and Coffee fees, Club Lottery fees, Bar fees, Equipment Hire fees, Raffle fees, Visiting Team fees, Match fees, Management fees, Competition fees, Car Park fees, Social Club Membership fees, Christmas Party fees, Reservation fees and a fee to cover all fees not listed in the above list of fees.

Therefore, all members are required to have a platinum credit card, membership of the Golf Club, drive a BMW, and retain stockholder shares in the local church restoration fund.

ADMINISTRATION

The Club is usually administrated by its Officers, President, Vice President, Past President, 'definitely past it' President, Chairman, Vice Chairman, Hon. Secretary, Hon. Treasurer, Hon. Competition Secretary, Captain, Vice Captain, Hon. Touring Team Secretary and several privileged club members.

The 'Board of Administration' will appoint a Management Committee, who in turn will appoint a Sub-committee, who in turn will appoint an Indoor committee, an Outdoor committee and a Selection committee, who in turn appoint a Social Committee, a Juniors committee and an Over-60's committee who in turn will appoint an Incoming committee who in turn will replace the outgoing committee who will apply to the members committee to be voted back in as the Administration board next season?

And that's just the beginning...................

ANNUAL AND OTHER GENERAL MEETINGS

The gathering of the clan, or quorum, to discuss, debate, make recommendations, give notice of motions, take votes, offer suggestions, ask opinions, enforce legislation, grant proxy, submit accounts, distribute reports, analyse balance sheets, evaluate performance and debate with club members over an extensive range of subjects.

Held for the duration of a lengthy evening in an ice cold club house without refreshments, the outcome of which is usually to do exactly the same as they did last year.

THE HON. SECRETARY

This person is a dedicated, enthusiast, quite capable of delivering a lengthy university lecture on the subject of paraphernalia.
They have memorised the entire 'potted' history of the club and its membership, including every score from every game, shot by shot, for the last five years.
They also manage to keep a record of every business transaction made in the preceding years, including Auntie Merritt's borrowing of 5p for a pack of pastilles on June 3rd eleven years ago.

THE HON. TREASURER

An exacting, precise, shy and introvert person, fanatical about figures, who can, given the opportunity, recite backwards the entire inventory of the club down to the last sheet of A4 paper. Their provisional summary of accounts often resembles a written paper on astral-physics for a university degree following translation into a foreign language.

Inquisitive bowlers asking pertinent questions are likely to be entertained by six hours of algebraic construction and mathematical formulation.

To protect your individual sanity just take it that the 'bottom line' is right, accept that the figures balance and you may get time for a cup of tea after the meeting!

THE COMMITTEE IN APPEAL

This is a representative board of individuals whose important role within the club is to adjudicate on disputes, internal confrontations, appeals, and applications for membership.

Such is the pleasure and prominence of these positions that the committee will 'sit' given the least provocation; last weeks adjourned mini-hearings included 'The Coffee Budget', "Why is a 4kg Bag of sugar a better buy then 2kg?" and "Is there really 500 sheets on a Co-op toilet roll?"

All adjudication is fair, unbiased, and binding as long as you remember to leave £50 under the chair on the way out.

DRESS

Members are encouraged to dress blandly in grey and white to avoid 'clashing' with the woods, now available in Flame Red, Banana Yellow, Day-Glo Green, Sky Blue and Jaffa Orange.

Members often revolt by covering their club blazers with as many emblems of office, lapel badges, and memorabilia as humanly possible. Club players find it easy to recognise officials in this way, as the more important they are, the more they stoop over, head bowed by the increasing weight of the chains of office.

A staggering, drunk-like apparition may, on closer inspection, prove to be the Club President in full regalia.

ALTERATION TO RULES

Submit recommendations to the AGM and best of luck!!!

RULES AND REGULATIONS

There are two main governing bodies that oversee the sport of bowling; of these the E.B.A. are the central figure. There are several differences in the running of the bodies but in essence, on the green, the most important key issues are as follows...

WOODS THAT TOUCH THE COT ARE CHALKED (EBA)

Never anything to worry yourself about as you will discover the percentage of woods that touch the cot are quite low. Even more so the number of bowls that are still touching the cot after all the bowls are played. You are more likely to be the furthest away because everyone will be after your wood. New bowlers may deliberately bowl to miss the cot in order to avoid damage from subsequent 'firing' woods. Your finances are guaranteed to be well protected though as the market for chalk is securely established and one stick will be good for at least five seasons.

CHALKED WOODS ARE LIVE IN THE DITCH (EBA)

Ok, you went and did it! You actually touched the cot and now your wood is adorned with a multitudinous amount of chalk graffiti or, worse still, 'sprayed on' spots that make it look like it caught the measles. Your wood has ended up in the ditch where it is quite safe, because the cot is probably still halfway up the green. The insinuation that woods are 'live' should not be taken too seriously. After 100 years of bowling there has yet to be an instance of any bowl sprouting arms and legs and climbing out of the ditch of its own account.

WOODS THAT TOUCH THE COT DO NOT GET CHALK (EBF)

In reality, the federation did not get a lucrative sponsorship deal with 'J. W. Whitestick Ltd' the only chalk manufacturing company. Therefore, in order to save costs the committee decided it would be a good idea to pretend it was an altogether better game not to have 'chalkers' at all. Therefore, the only reward you get for a perfectly drawn wood is the pleasure of watching the next bowler knocking it off with much gusto.

THE MAT MAY BE MOVED UP THE GREEN (EBA)

The mat has a great number of uses apart from that as a picnic site for your baby girl's annual outing with her doll collection. You may move the mat at your discretion as a tactical ploy from the two metre mark up and down the rink as long as you have left enough distance to cast the cot no less than 75ft. However, you should remember not to move the mat during play, as the other players might get upset, especially if you try to move them whilst one is still standing on it.

FOUR WOODS ARE USED IN SINGLES (EBA)

So much flexibility, just imagine? you can put one wood in the ditch, bowl another with wrong bias, still another can roll effortlessly into the rose bed and yet, when you are three down with one wood left you still have the chance to bowl a perfect wood. The chances are that you will bowl 'shot wood' and upset the opponents who held three good shots until then, or alternatively draw to the cot for shot, fall over nudging the cot and end up going four down...oh well that's bowls!

THE MAT MAY NOT BE MOVED UP THE GREEN (EBF)

Somewhat simplifying the game, much like taking the back row off a chessboard, this immediately leaves all beginners with a worsening dilemma. They are suddenly faced with the task of throwing a heavy, non-complying cannonball the length of a lawn that suddenly seems to be the size of a football pitch. Given that your total concentration is devoted to the task of not dropping the wood on your toe whilst everyone else watches, you invariably overcompensate and trip over the edge of the mat instead. Flat on your face, you may reflect on the sudden absence of your wood and your similarity to the Hunchback of Notre Dame as more than a coincidence.

TWO WOODS ARE USED IN SINGLES (EBF)

With only two woods to bowl, the tactical game goes straight out of the window. This is a 'sudden death' nearest to the cot with only two chances. You may find this a very fast game, indeed more experienced players try to play this game very quickly to keep their opponent off balance. You will suddenly realise on the twelfth end that you are changing ends so quickly you are reaching the other end, and the cot, before your last wood does.

ALL WOODS ON THE RINK COUNT (EBA)

It doesn't matter how badly your bowls were played or where they ended up, as long as they are still 'live' they could conceivably still count. Although the opportunity for a wood ten metres away to eventually become shot is remote, it does happen. It is inevitable that a short wood will be hit by the following seven woods, knocking it closer and closer until it ends up as a dubious measure!

WOODS ARE DEAD IN THE DITCH (EBF)

Guaranteed to put the 'fear of god' in you when bowling a heavy wood, and you may need to pray for divine intervention as it approaches the lip of the ditch without any indication of slowing down. As part of a new coaching initiative, any 'live' wood falling into the ditch will summarily be executed by firing squad. The player will therefore have to bowl the next end with just one wood, forcing them to try harder.

ANY WOOD MORE THAN TWO METRES AWAY FROM THE COT DOES NOT COUNT (EBF)

Supposedly, a way of improving the game by encouraging you to bowl nearer to the jack, therefore increasing your accuracy. In reality a great way of making a one-hour game last all day thus avoiding the inconvenience of getting home early enough to cut the grass or cook the tea. After 44 ends, the score tied at 3 – 3, you realise that its going to take a lot of practice just to reach the other end of the green without the further complication of having to try and get within two metres of the cot. Experienced bowlers tend to find, with only the 'draw' shot to play they usually fall asleep after the seventh end anyway.

What do you mean, "We only have one cot"?

HOW TO PLAY THE GAME

PICKING YOUR BOWLS

It is very easy to pick a set of woods, not quite so easy to pick a set that will actually do you any good.

Perhaps it's best to remember to try the woods out before committing to purchase them? Otherwise, you may bowl better with them left in the box, or better still just bowl the box!

Bowls are available in eight sizes, briefly defined as follows

SIZE	0	*Pass the microscope!*
SIZE	1	*About the size of a malteser, just as fragile...*
SIZE	2	*Onto a golf ball, don't forget to shout 'fore'*
SIZE	3	*Orange; certainly may a-peel to you?*
SIZE	4	*Galia melon; watch out for firing shots!!*
SIZE	5	*Football, Can you 'Bend it like Beckham?'*
SIZE	6	*Medicine Ball; this is the heavyweight!*
SIZE	7	*Tenpin Bowl, Ok, now you need two hands!*
SIZE	8	*OH MY GOD!!! You have got to be kidding!!*

Bowls are also available in 'medium weight' or, if you prefer, 'heavy weight', which will increase your swing but make it harder to play straight 'running' woods.

Now all you have to do is decide which of the many available 'makes' you prefer, based on the manufacturers preference for swinging or straight-line woods.

And finally, after three days of indecision and a near nervous breakdown all you have to do is pick a colour???

Oh yes! *That's right, you are no longer tied to dull black or even the rich classy brown, so go ahead and make your choice, there's Red, Yellow, Blue, Green, Orange, Pink and Purple ...*

Pass the sunglasses!!!

EQUIPMENT & BOWLING

Ok, so you've picked your new bowls and you still have some money left, so how about those important extras?

You'll need the following just to get started...

SHOES *Special flat-bottomed footwear that will take you back to the 70's and vivid memories of those platforms...*

In fact, you may feel like wearing the shoeboxes instead!!

Initially you can be quite flamboyant and select from an extensive colour range of brown, brown, or brown...

Why not be adventurous?

Opt for those racy slip-ons instead of laces!!

WATERPROOFS *Yes, it does rain and invariably it will rain every time you step on the green during May and June!*
Do purchase something slightly more substantial and durable than a supermarket plastic bag.

THERMAL UNDERWEAR *You cannot possibly imagine how cold you will get on a spring evening at 9pm in a Northeasterly gale after two hours!!*

MEASURE *Just in case you DO manage to get a wood close in the first six months, you may want to indulge in the pleasure of 'measuring for shot', if only for future reference.*
Go ahead, enjoy all the delight of 'heated debate' about 'who's holding shot'; the prospect of impassioned, frenzied negotiation before entertaining the illustrious presence of the Umpire!

BOWLS BAG *Well you do want to protect your newfound pride and joy, don't you?*
Prices range from bargain basement 'string nets' to 'mid-range' holdall or full scale 'champions bag' which includes space for thermos, sandwiches, hip flask, last years champions trophy and mascot!

CHALK *Don't go mad and buy too much, a small carton of six sticks should cover the first five years in fact it'll probably cover your whole club membership!*

GRIPPO *Having purchased your woods which, after stepping on the green, you may find were perhaps a little bit optimistic in size, you now need some assistance in surreptitiously holding on to them.*

There are many bowlers' secret recipes such as 'Rose Water and Glycerine' but you may run in to problems trying out 'blue tac' or superglue.

Purchase a tube of 'Grippo' immediately but do NOT get it mixed up with your cream for piles.

CHAMOIS LEATHER *In the middle of a tropical rainstorm on a Sunday afternoon, when you can only see the other end of the green by adding 'windscreen wiper' attachments to your glasses, you may appreciate the practicality of a good 'old fashioned' chamois leather rather than the sodden excuse for a dry cloth in your equally wet trouser pocket.*

WAXED CLOTH *Not so much as an item readily available 'off the shelf', but the outcome of a typical, bar-mat sized towel after five years of waxing your woods on a weekly basis.*

A good 'waxed cloth' is measured by its ability to stand up of its own accord on one edge. Indeed, it is quite possible to contrive a number of unique origami positions with the cloth.

WAXED GLOVE *One of the newer novelty effects, imagine trying to bowl in a pair of sticky oven gloves?*

HEATED PAD *A rather clever liquid-filled pad that, when pressed in the middle, solidifies giving off heat for a period of up to thirty minutes.*

There is nothing better, in the middle of a very cold, wet, miserable evening of bowling then using one of these to get the blood racing through your fingertips.

Be warned though, by the time you get all feeling back and have recovered from the 'pins and needles' effect, you'll have burnt all your fingertips on the 'superheat' portable reactor and your bowling hand will be glowing more than the local light house.

In the interests of preserving 'endangered species' please do not upset the local glow-worm population with your sudden spontaneous illuminations.

JOINING A CLUB

Invariably the best way to better your game, learn about the sport and progress to the next stage; this is the 'holy grail', that we come to revere as 'County Bowling'!

You can now feel much at home amongst the other 49 players because you are virtually guaranteed that at least half of them are no better or no worse than you.

At last, here is the opportunity, a genuine chance to win a game or maybe two without the pressure of drawing a shot!

Your 'faithful friend' 'Mr Access Card' by your side, you pay your club membership and realise there are a few accessories you now need to purchase.

After all, you can no longer turn out to play in your favourite 'Bermuda' shorts and nostalgic 'Iron Maiden' T-Shirt.

Instead, you are now required to look every bit the 'gentleman' in grey trousers and white shirt, (preferably with stiff collar) to which you may add the privilege of a club tie and tie pin!

Of course, you should buy a club badge in case you get the opportunity to play as a representative for the club against other teams...so all you need now is a new 'blazer' to sew the badge to...

Back to your 'flexible friend' again!

Perhaps you have higher ambitions and pursue the dream of reaching a quarter final or further?

Well you ought to buy a pair of white trousers just in case, and, if you are feeling flamboyant splash out on a pair of white bowling shoes to match...

Don't forget some new white socks!!

You really ought to think about the possibility of those weather changes and purchase one or two white jumpers; you'll need short and long sleeved just in case!

Wouldn't it be nice to have a lightweight jacket or short-sleeved fleece as well?

White of course!!!

Now you can return home victorious, resplendent in all your new purchases, ready for your first day of playing at 'The Bowling Club'.

Don't forget on the way home to buy your wife, or partner, a nice bunch of flowers...

After all, you have just spent the next three months mortgage payments on bowling!

HOLDING THE BOWL

On the assumption that you have indeed, with the help of a knowledgeable bowling assistant, purchased the correct size bowl for your hand?

You thought that was the hard part over didn't you?

All you have to do is pick up the wood and bowl it, the rest is easy and you will soon be a champion!

WRONG!

First of all, you need to learn to grip the wood, there are of course several styles so which should you use?

THE CRADLE GRIP

The bowl rests loosely in the palm of your hand with your fingers extended under the face of the bowl.
A nice, easy bowling method, easy to bowl and equally easy to lose all control of, be prepared to watch your wood travel to every corner of the green!

THE CLAW GRIP

As before but with your thumb raised up on the top of the 'grip-line'. More difficult to master perhaps, but much easier for controlling the wood.

Inexperienced players may, at the last minute, develop a nervous twitch in the guiding thumb and, as a result, the wood may take an alarming diversion sideways across the rink.

THE FINGER/THUMB GRIP

As before but with your thumb gripping the top centremost point of the wood, the most difficult to master but superlative for the perfect controlled wood and delicate drawing shots.

Be aware that hesitating on the mat with the grip may cause muscle cramp at the base of the thumb resulting in the wood remaining where it is even after going through the motions of bowling it.

Quickly hide the offending hand (and wood) behind your back and proclaim that "you must have bowled it too fast and it's probably already in the other ditch!"
Upon visiting the head use any distraction to place the offending wood in the nearby ditch as soon as possible.
One such method is to cause female members to faint as you march up the green with the 'bulging' bowl hidden indiscreetly in your trouser pocket!

THE CAPES GRIP

A very rare, not often used bowling grip. As old age, arthritis and muscle fatigue creep in and eyesight begins to dwindle there is always the CAPES grip.

Hold the wood with two hands and hurl it with great gusto up the green, much in the manner of Geoff Capes, legendary shot putter, after whom this technique is so aptly named.

The resulting impression of a Barnes Wallis 'bouncing bomb' as it traverses the green may produce a recitation of 'the dam busters' theme from your team and a look of panic from the green-keeper as he eyes the damage to his beloved green.

Don't forget, when holding the bowl, there is a bias or 'weighted' side so always make sure you have the small centre circle on the inside of your hand.

Failure to observe this simple action will result in the bowl acting rather like a boomerang, turning away from the cot and you may endure a large shout of 'DRINKS ALL AROUND' from the amused on-lookers.

DELIVERY

OK, how are you doing?

Not a nervous wreck yet?

So you've mastered the wood and the grip?

Well done!   Now for the delivery...

The basic and very simple idea is that you step forward off the mat with one foot, as a rule the side opposite to the bowling hand, not the nearest!

As you step forward you would usually bend down slightly bracing your 'non bowling' hand on your extended knee whilst bringing your bowling hand through a prescribed arc in a controlled fashion until releasing the bowl as your fingertips brush the top of the grass.

In reality, any of the following are more likely to happen...

A)   You forget to bend and the wood descends from a height of three feet lodging into the green like a rampant meteorite.

B)   You forget to let go until the very last moment; the bowl takes off like an orbiting space shuttle to land half way up the green

C)   You miss the bracing leg and fall over.

D)   You bend too low, impacting on the green, breaking all your fingernails and leaving gouge marks in the green.

There are a number of stances from which to bowl off the mat, each has their own supporters and practitioners.

ATHLETIC As described above, standing upright on the mat, slight bend to the knees (optional), step forward and bowl.

CROUCH Crouched down on the mat and rising up to deliver the bowl, a position usually recommended with a well-stoked pipe in the mouth. Do not try this with a wooden leg!

FIXED *Standing on the mat, leg already extended in the stride, hand locked on knee before bowling.*

With all deliveries do always remember to let go of the wood, keep eyes focused on the 'aiming point', retain one foot on the mat whilst bowling, pray that the seat of your trousers does not rip during delivery and keep your 'high fibre' diet under control at all times.

LINE AND LENGTH

Well, you've nearly arrived at the finish line.....

Have you mastered the delivery?

Are you dressed for the occasion?

Feeling 'at one' with your woods?

If you answered YES to all these... Well Done!

Only three small, insignificant things stand between you and the instantaneous success you so richly deserve...

'Line', 'Length' and 'Drawing the shot'!

LINE

The 'line' that the bowl travels as it prescribes a perfect 'arc' towards the 'cot' should be the simplest thing in the world to find. After all what could be easier than picturing the 'curve' and sending your bowl along it?

Well, before you get carried away remember these points!

1) The distance between the cot and the bowl will change every time the cot is bowled or the mat is moved, therefore the arc will move and the line will change.

2) The line will also change depending on the weather conditions, including rain, wind, hailstorm, and sunshine, all of which will affect the playing surface.

3) The line is always different between your forehand and backhand... Did we mention this yet?

Well, your forehand is the same as the side you hold the wood in and the backhand is the opposite side (therefore, bowling with your left hand to the left of the cot is forehand, to the right of the cot is backhand, reverse the options for bowling with your right hand).

Do remember this very important piece of information that reminds you to turn the wood over when you change from bowling backhand to forehand or vice-versa.

Unless of course you do like purchasing copious quantities of alcoholic beverage for other people to enjoy???

4) The line will be altered by greens being played 'on rink' and 'off rink'. This basically is a cunning plan contrived by the green keeper more to keep you on your toes than to preserve the grass.

Every morning at 9am, he will sneak out on to the green and move all the 'rink markers' up or down the green. Worse still, every other day he turns the whole green around so you play the other way, North to South, rather than East to West.

The bottom line is, unless you have an I.Q. great enough to apply to MENSA and have a photographic memory as well, you are never going to calculate all the possible permutations.

5) Every green you play on will be different depending on how well kept they are. Some may play like an ice rink, but have you ever tried bowling on a ploughed potato field? You will!

By the way, did you realise that greens can be different sizes?

LENGTH

Quite simply, there is a minimum length, 75ft, and a maximum length, because of the ditch. Other than that, you will be required to bowl your wood, on the hand of your choice, as near as possible to the cot.

There is no such thing as a good or bad length as you should be able to bowl to any length, but always be aware of the length that you find more suited to your game.

Do you prefer a short cot where you can see everything, and, more importantly, hit everything when you need to?

Do you prefer a long cot, somewhere in the distant haze, knowing that you can reach with ease and perhaps your opponent will struggle or can't even see it?

You should always have, at the back of your mind, a preferred length, the one that you have practised on, week in week out, making it your 'ace in the hole' on which you are 'supreme', 'unbeatable', 'king of kings', 'master of the universe';

Well at least capable of getting one wood close...

SHOTS

You've come this far, you are still not deterred?

Well done! You are nearly a bowler!

The last hurdle lies before you...

In any game you play, however it's played, albeit as a practice, a friendly roll up, or competitive match, the 'finishing post' is what matters, and to get there you need to score shots!

Now probably they haven't mentioned this to you yet, but the person playing against you will be scoring shots as well!!

They may be polite, friendly, and gentlemanly, with a pleasant manner, a warm disposition, and courteous conduct.

But underneath there is a satanic, burning desire to win, to win well, to beat you, to grind you into the dust, leaving you battered, bruised and broken on the bowling green after 27 minutes, having lost 21-nil.

This isn't just a game....

It's a war, with cunning strategies, feints, duplicity, and manoeuvres worthy of a Field Commander in the Napoleonic wars.

Imagine you are playing a game of chess on grass, every piece important, strategic, and purposeful.

Remember, like a general, you can march up to the 'battlefield', to view your 'troops' and consider your opportunities before reaping carnage with your next wood.

Enjoy the cut and thrust of the game, always say "well done" through gritted teeth when your opponent bowls well, shake hands before the match, remembering to tightly hold their bowling hand in a lengthy vice-like, bone-breaking grip.

Apologise when that 'coughing fit' strikes you just as the opponent is about to bowl a very important wood.

Plead a sudden, mysterious ailment, muscle injury, cramp or woeful story if you are in serious trouble in the game, the opponent may feel sorry for you and 'ease up'.

Always remember there IS someone who can bowl better than you so never take any one for granted... next time you walk out onto the green have a closer look!

Is your first opponent, 'stooped with old age, using a walking frame, wearing thick spectacles, has a long grey beard and Queen Victoria's picture stamped on his woods?

Well, he has probably been bowling for 75 years and can place a wood on the cot with his eyes shut!

He may even be Mervyn King's Great Granddad!!!

Never take anyone for granted, not unless you enjoy losing on a regular basis.

After closer inspection, the bowlers had to agree that the bowling was not up to their usual standard.

BOWLING TERMS

AIMING POINT. Traditionally an estimated point about ¾ of the way along the projected 'arc' of the wood as it travels the length of the green.

In reality, depending on the bowling, this point often 'wanders' and becomes the rink marker, an attractive piece of grass edging on the ditch, a particularly striking flower in the club rose-bed or Mrs Jones' kneecap as she lazes resplendent in a deckchair.

The resulting reactions by the bowled wood often end up with the disturbance of 'heads' on the wrong rink, decapitation of the gardeners prized rose or worse still Mrs Coddle (eligible spinster) needing a strong cup of tea after a near miss!

ARC. Geometrically, in a perfect world, the line of curvature described by the bowl, in reality one that resembles a large worm pursued by a hungry seagull with its legs tied together.

BACK WOOD. In theory, a well placed tactical wood that is the furthest wood behind the cot in the direction of the ditch.

In reality, it is usually the wood that's in the ditch!

In fact, as green speeds increase during the summer season it is often found that all the woods bowled are back woods!

The last player bowling after all previous woods have ended in the ditch will find themselves somewhat under pressure!!

Members often compete for the honour of holding the best back wood; the current record holder placed his on the A12 that runs past the clubhouse!!

BANK (1). This was originally the place where you used to have money before you went out and purchased all your new bowling kit.

(2). This refers to the slightly raised embankment at the back of the 'ditch'.

You should be seriously concerned if the green keeper owns a J.C.B. and expect the inclusion of drawbridges, battlements, and ramparts, also the possibility of a few siege cannons.

BIAS. *The original term for the weighted side of a bowl that gives the wood bias or turn.*
More recently used as a bowlers curse when woods go against the run of the green for no apparent reason other than that the bowler has probably bowled the wood upside down. A call for 'drinks all round' from the other team does little to lessen the embarrassment.

BLOCK. *Not an indication of a type of shot, reviewed later in this book, but a bowling reference to a team.*
A block is the correct term for a number of bowlers, usually 3, or 4, that form a loose cartel.
Hence the reason a badly performing skip is often humorously known as a Block Head!

BOWL. *Something cold, lifeless, unforgiving, frustrating, and alien in the hand that never pays any attention to your demands.*
Neglected wives often feel much the same about their bowling partner and may express a preference to sleeping with their woods.

BOWLS FESTIVAL. *Take two hundred bowlers and squeeze them onto a small number of greens in heavy rain four times a day until 198 have collapsed through hunger, exhaustion and hypothermia.*
Take the remaining two, who are by now 'nervous wrecks' and place them in front of the assembled, highly critical, 198 bowlers with, assorted press, judges and County selectors.
Wait until ambulance has left with the two finalists and then repeat formula for Pairs, Triples, Fours and any other combinations.

CALLIPERS. *After fifteen minutes of heated discussion over the width of a 'cigarette paper' between two 'shot' woods the call for callipers often leads to a rosé cheeked and exuberant Umpire leaping to his feet brandishing his treasured, well oiled, antique mechanics!*

CAST / CAST THE JACK. *Not related to 'fly fishing' by J R Hartley nor perhaps even a television angling program with a famous 60's football player. In truth the ability to 'cast' or roll the 'cot' in a straight line to a prescribed length using the more favoured stance deliveries such as:-*

EYES CLOSED
Anywhere on the green will do

CLAMPED FIST
Failure to let go results in a fruitless search for a lost cot and the inspection of four suspicious mushrooms.

OPEN PALM
Usually reaches ten feet resulting in a re-cast

CHUCK "N' CHANCE
Never heard of playing a tactical length

BACKWARD TOSS
It always ends up in the ditch three feet behind you but at least you can bowl to the cot easily

CENTRING THE COT. The traditional, often amusing pastime of 'placing the cot' on the 'centre line' after delivery.

As the cot is never bowled in a straight line, the distances it invariably needs to be moved can be up to several metres.

The 'marker' then contrives to place the cot by any means other than the use of his hand just to make life interesting and his natural instinct for 'measurement' immediately eludes him.

Subsequent shuffling back and forth across the green has been known to occupy fifteen minutes, enough time for the rest of the team to leave the green, have a cup of tea, go to the toilet and return for the 'grand finale'.

CHALKER. Every 'skips' dream; the opportunity to become 'Picasso' and indulge in freehand artwork on a bowlers wood with an array of chalk or graffiti spray; hence the reason that so many bowlers will shun playing well, thus avoiding the risk of placing any wood dangerously near to the cot.

Never invite Rolf Harris to play; your bowl may end up in the Tate Gallery!

CHANGING ENDS. A memorable, graceful display often better performed by the larger groups of bowlers known as 'TRIPLES' or 'FOURS'.

This visually dramatic routine peaks as the two teams approach one another from opposite ends of the green.

Dependant upon which team is winning at that point there will be exquisite vocal exchanges and subtle physical interactions such as 'undoing of shoelaces', 'hair pulling', 'shirt tugging', 'treading on of toes' and 'rib digging'.

CLUBHOUSE. *A low lying building with lots of glasses, cups, biscuit tins, out-of-date bowling notices, hopeful requests of completion dates, lost ties, single left shoes, an antique tea urn and a much used mini-bar for purposes of mutual consolation.*

COACH. *A person who has not endured enough suffering in their life yet, they have therefore turned to the dark path of instruction and meditation.*
Armed with the knowledge of all rules, regulations, method, and practicality they proceed to instruct novices with often-hilarious results.

COMPETITIONS. *See 'EBA / EBF tournaments & festivals'*

COT. *The little white thing that bowlers spend all of their life trying to hit at a distance where they can't even see it and probably would not hit unless it was the size of a beach ball.*

COUNT. *Nothing at all to do with vampires, this is in fact a reference to the part of the game when things can get a little tense as you debate on the subject of 'who is holding shot?' and 'how many?'*
You may find the following guide is a good indication of the state of play,

1 DOWN	*... OK they were lucky, its only one shot!*
2 DOWN	*... At least my woods are together in the ditch!!*
3 DOWN	*... Looks as if I took the wrong wood out?*
4 DOWN	*... Perhaps firing wasn't the best option?*
5 DOWN	*... At least I have one wood on the green!*
6 DOWN	*... Don't worry I still hold shot on the next rink!*
7 DOWN	*... Anyone fancy a game of golf?*
8 DOWN	*... Distract them, I'll start the car!!*

DEAD END. *The principle requiring an end to be replayed under certain 'rules of engagement' when the cot, upon being struck, has been moved into the next rink.*
Depending on the speed and accuracy of the intended strike, the offending cot has been known to relocate to the adjacent rose-bed, the next green, and even the main road on the other side of the hedgerow.
The purpose of this strike is often lost on the team because they were usually the ones holding 'shot' until this instance of 'temporary insanity' by their own 'skip'.

DEAD WOOD. *Nothing to do with the famous Indian pursuit of a western stagecoach, but the equally pointless exercise of playing your wood in such a way that it misses everything and ends up in the ditch.*

Worse still if your previous perfectly placed shot wood is struck by the next players 'cannonball' and is promptly propelled into the ditch at great speed usually with several others.

Your only saviour is to obtain a perfect draw; you will be rewarded with 'the mark of Zorro' etched into your wood by your appreciative skip.

Be warned that sneaky skips may attempt to knock your 'chalker' out of rink and have it declared 'dead'.

DITCH. *A receptacle for collecting a variety of 'impact lessening' devices such as corks, sponge nets, underlay off-cuts and golf balls in the vain attempt at slowing down life-threatening 'firing' bowls.*

Also a great place to hide those embarrassing 'draw' shots, bowled on such a narrow line, that miss by ten metres or worse still are so tight they are rolling across the next rink and into their ditch!

DITCH THE JACK. *A rather desperate ploy of 'firing' the jack into the ditch because that's where your nearest wood is!! Alternative literal interpretations have led to the competition secretary being in need of a helping hand on several occasions.*

DOLLY. *Possibly a lady of ill repute much mentioned in dark corners around the clubhouse, always guaranteed to raise a guilty smile on the green when a shout of 'on the dolly' goes up from the lead bowler.*

E.B.A. *The governing body, the English Bowling Association, founded in 1903 by the famous cricketer Dr. W. G. Grace.*

It is often wondered if some bowlers actually think they are delivering a cricket ball when playing their wood, given the number of bounces and deviations made.

E.B.F. *This is an alternative, less widespread form of bowling, managed under different rules and regulations, known in full as the English Bowling Federation.*

So named apparently because of their founder members great admiration for STAR TREK movies and adoption of 'Klingon' style aggressive game tactics on the bowling green.

FOOT FAULT. *To be avoided at all costs, the act of taking your feet off the mat before the bowl has left your hand.*

At all times one foot, usually the back foot, must maintain contact with the mat surface.

Hilarity often ensues when an overstretching bowler performs an action worthy of a triple or long jump champion whilst trying to maintain control of their wood and dignity at the same time as ensuring their foot remains in place.

The use of glue, chewing gum, and blue tack to maintain a firm contact is frowned upon and often discovered as the guilty party attempts to hobble up the green with the mat still firmly attached to their offending foot.

A foot fault may also be called if the player attempts to bowl in incorrect attire such as brothel creepers, Wellington boots, or fluffy slippers.

GAMESMANSHIP. *A clever name for flexible verbal litigation between bowlers, no kicking, gouging, spitting or shirt pulling is allowed, but cries of 'I KNOW WHERE YOUR WIFE WAS LAST NIGHT', as the lead is about to bowl, is a keen favourite.*

GREEN. *A number of RINKS of any size shape and colour often resembling a patchwork square most recently used by the 7th Cavalry for troop manoeuvres prior to any match.*

GREEN BOWLING. *A loose term for an 'all weather' exterior surface, made up from grasses of various lengths and shades interspersed with pigeon droppings, dirt patches and small holes that would not look out of place on a putting green.*

Depending on the time of year these greens can be found underwater; later on in the season a bowlers favourite pastime is to indulge in a friendly game of 'spot the grass blade'.

GREEN SPEED. *Nothing at all to do with the green keepers personal hobby of planting 'illegal substances' on the green, which he secretly harvests every morning before 9am.*

This is actually the term for judging just how long a bowl will take to reach the cot after delivery; to confuse non-bowlers it is fair to say that the faster the green the longer the wood takes to reach the cot!

In reality, some bowlers' woods may never reach the cot and on more than one occasion, it has been known for the skip to put away his stopwatch and take out a calendar.

GRASSING THE BOWL. Supposedly the time honoured skill of delivering the perfect wood in such a way that you 'grass the bowl' as it leaves your hand, gliding gently over the surface in a controlled fashion......

More often relates to a clumsier delivery that tends to dig gouges into the green surface, thus coating the bowl with a liberal amount of grass, soil, and worm heads.

Sometimes a reference to the much suffering skip who has the unenvied task of informing the captain of the fact that you have successfully denuded the rink of anything resembling grass and you now have four green woods in the ditch (again!).

The astonished captain is left speechless by your miniature model of the Grand Canyon in front of the delivery mat.

GREYS. A dull, coarsely woven fabric for the purpose of covering an assortment of knobbly knees, varicose veins, bowling bruises, and hairy legs.

Player's interpretation of the colour grey provides an interesting source of conversation whilst they studiously ponder over 'swatch' fabric colour charts during the team break.

Members undisclosed 'colour blindness' is often discovered inadvertently when they turn up to play in banana coloured trousers and a Hawaiian shirt.

GRIPPO. A treacle-like substance smeared on woods to assist any bowler who has hence discovered that they are using a bowl that is at least three sizes too big and weighs more than the average shopping bag full of groceries.

HEAD. A loose term given to a collection of bowls, spread, usually over a very wide area roughly the size of a barn door. A request to 'visit the head' can often lead to much confusion for any bowler currently in need of sanitary relief.

This unfortunate term for a collection of woods in a set area often creates a number of light-hearted incidents that the long-suffering 'skip' has to accept the responsibility for.

'Skips' should remember it is unwise to invite members of the team to 'fire at his head'.

Invitations offered to 'examine the head' should be treated cautiously and a wary eye should be kept open at all times for bowlers approaching, dressed in white, one hand behind their back and wearing a stethoscope.

ILLEGAL CAST. _Taking the skill of 'casting the cot' one step further, this is the official term given to a delivery that results in the cot being shorter than the permitted length from the mat, or, worse still, ending up out of rink altogether._

A cot seen travelling at great speed along the green will have an equally greater affect on the 'lead' as he visibly wilts under the withering eye of the 'skip'.

The closer the cot gets to the edge of the ditch the greater the effect.

At 'twenty shots all' and a crucial end, the cot teetering on the edge of the rink in an uncertain fashion can often reduce both 'skips' and 'leads' to jabbering idiots.

All manner of niggling coughs, foot movement, loud exuberant expressions, and excessive hand warming will be indulged in by the opposition 'skip' in an 'innocent' attempt to persuade the cot to fall into the ditch.

INDOOR BOWLING. _A converted barn with a bowling surface much like an ice-skating rink. Bowlers on Rink 1 often hold shot on Rink 6 due to the fact there is more 'bend' on the carpet than on a football pitch with David Beckham playing._

JACK. _Nothing to do with the cot, actually the name of the Captains much hated 'best mate' who ran off with his wife. Thereafter giving rise to the much-vented shout of 'Jack' every time he fires._

LINE. _This is supposed to represent the correct route you should take with your bowl from the 'mat' to the 'cot' in order to gain shot._

In fact your bowl would have had a greater chance of 'being placed' on the London-Piccadilly line!

Well at least it would have reached a destination, eventually!!

LIGNUM. _In 'olden days' prior to the successful development of composite bowls, came the era of Sir Francis Drake and the truly 'wooden' wood._

Did you really think that all those round holes in trees were only made by woodpeckers???

'LIVE' BOWL. _Would you please give up the idea that bowls have a mind of their own, suggesting that they are 'alive' and will come back to haunt us as "THE STEPFORD WOODS"_

LENGTH. Causing many a blush and tittering around the ladies of the bowling club when the shout goes up from an excited 'skip' of "Well done partner that's a good length!!"

MASTER BOWL. Originally the unique 'template' from which all other bowls are mastered or checked for size, weight, curvature, and accuracy.

In darker quarters those that believe in 'live' woods talk in hushed tones of the 'Master' as a mythological character who was the 'Father of all sports' probably related to the Daleks.

MAT. A rectangular piece of rubber or latex roughly the size of Kylie Minogue's mini dress and no indication whatsoever that the Vice Captain, also known as Matt, is a cross-dresser.

MATCH. A competitive, friendly, gentleman's game often known as a 'free for all'. Also a small stick for setting fire to the seat of opponents trousers at crucial moments.

MEASURE. A small piece of string in a large white box capable of adapting to a multitude of different measures from the same distance depending on who is administering the measure.

PERCENTAGE PLAY. In all games, with every delivery there are several options as to which shot to play next. Beware of players who carry calculators, slide rules, and portable laptops on the bowling green.

Serious bowlers will often be found kneeling in front of the head, assessing the wind factor, mass acceleration, impact inertia, G-force, and grass gradients.

PLACING THE JACK. A simple task often mistaken for that of picking up the club competition secretary (also known as Jack) off the floor immediately in front of the bar and placing him on the nearest settee.

In fact, this is the much easier undertaking of placing the cot on a straight line between the mat and the ditch marker.

PLAYERS HANDICAP. A generic term for a system of penalising better players in a competition so that all players may effectively start on a level footing.

Learner bowlers desperate to at least 'score a shot' or claim a 'scalp' often find that they have a plus score of 20 shots to nil before even playing a wood.

The biggest mistake, at this stage, is to foolishly boast about your ability to beat the entire England team single–handed.
The 'handicapped' other player, will probably be the newly crowned County champion and recently selected for England.
A subsequent scoring of four shots an end for five ends may suddenly dampen the new player's ardour.
Indeed the possibility of 'losing the game' with only one wood left in their hands and 'game against' often results in a number of nervous breakdowns, mental disintegration and an inability to hold the wood due to excessively sweating hands.

POSITIONAL SHOT. A variation of the tactical wood, which is used to cover certain outcomes if the 'head' is likely to be altered, for example by a firing shot.
The tactical wood is always pre-announced and played for; whilst the positional shot is one that is announced after the wood has come to rest.
Hence a variety of poor shots that fall short or are overplayed, underplayed, tight, wide, or truly awful are re-classified as 'positional shots'.
Whilst this saves the bowler from a degree of embarrassment there is an element of disbelief from the rest of the team as they view the wood resting by the ditch, next to the rink marker, twelve feet away from the head.

RECOVERY SHOT. Essentially a shot to save a forlorn position that wouldn't look out of place on the field at Waterloo. You are facing several shots against and this is the only sensible shot to play in order to cut down the count.
This shot should not be attempted if you have a 'pacemaker' or suffer from any other serious or life-threatening ailment.

RESCUE SHOT. Slightly worse than a recovery shot, usually played by a 'skip' who simply cannot 'draw' to save his life.
His response to 'shots against' will be to deliver a 'firing shot' that effectively leaves burn marks on the grass and takes three days for the dust to settle before judging the outcome from the resultant impact.

RINK. A rectangular piece of grass that keeps moving every day, theoretically to keep the grass fresh, in reality to prevent any bowler from getting near the cot on a regular basis.

RINK FEE. A daily donation to the clubs most supported 'charitable' fund: - keeping the bar well stocked!

ROLL UP. The differences between having a friendly game of bowls and making your own cigarette cannot be confused. When is the last time you saw anyone with a No.5 bowl in a Ritzla paper?

A roll up comes in many variations one of them a three player game where two bowlers 'team up' against the single player.

They have to score 21 shots against his 7, but they do have double the number of woods and they WILL fire if he holds a shot, which is rare enough anyway!

SELECTOR. A rare and endangered species that comes in three varieties, Club, County, or National. NEVER say anything that might remotely offend, upset, or otherwise physically or mentally disturb this person.

It is wise to remember their birthday, wife's name, wedding anniversary and anything else of importance as your bowling destiny now lies in their hands.

SHORT MAT. The Vice Captains younger brother.

SPRING THE JACK. The poor old Competition Secretary comes in for a lot of stick in the club from every quarter.

This is no indication of any members desire to attach a large coiled spring to the rear of Jack and bounce him all over the green like Zebedee.

The inference is simply that of altering the 'head' in such a way that your bowl causes the 'cot' to move away from the shot wood it was previously touching or close to.

STANCE. Originally a term used for the position taken on the mat prior to bowling; more recently a phrase used by partying members as a drunken invitation in the local nightclub.

TAPE. The Umpire's prized possession, used initially to check the distance of a 'cast' of the cot.

Often ends up in a 'tug of war' between the skips attempting to extract the very last inch out of the measure, much to the amusement of the rest of the team.

Subsequent rewinding of the tape lead to the discovery that it is suddenly three inches longer than it was previously!

TARGET BOWLS. *The inspiration behind a lunatic fringe of frustrated archery fanatics.*
Place a rubberised archery target flat on the bowling green and then try to place your woods on it by bowling them as normal.
You may notice that the woods have a tendency to catch the lip of the mat and roll right around it!
It is not recommended that you attempt to imitate the antics of Robin Hood by delivering your wood from a crossbow or longbow.
Your heavily bandaged foot will be a big giveaway to other bowlers of how you have probably spent your weekend and a plea of 'gout' will not be taken seriously!

TEA BREAK. *In any friendly match, there is a point, usually mid-way through a competition, when bowlers are summoned off the green for a refreshing cup of tea and a quality selection of ancient biscuits.*
Bowlers are warned against taking a second cup, as the long-standing urn will now be brewed to the consistency of paint stripper.
Do NOT ever go into a tea break as the winning team on your rink at that stage.
Without exception after the tea break, the game 'turns around' and you will lose every subsequent shot, measure, and end.
Winning skips, ahead in the first half will often try to encourage their team to establish an impregnable lead, enough to offset losing four shots an end after the tea break.
Nevertheless, they know that the feared call of "TEA UP" will still see them tied level, with one bowl to go on the last end!

THE SOUTH AFRICAN CLINIC. *Absolutely no reference to the recent club tour of the European and Southern states, which began in Amsterdam and ended in Cape Town.*
True, press rumours did indicate many members were 'enjoying the culture' and several did indeed succumb to a sudden outbreak of 'measles'.
Apart from the comedy of watching 'leads' bowl whilst apparently suffering from a large intake of 'itching powder', detailed information was not more forthcoming for the press.
A later public statement released by the committee referred to the name as a form of bowling stance developed by Dr Julius Serge; the pressroom collapsed in hysterical laughter.

TIED END. _Usually descriptive of an 'end' of bowls where the shots are inseparable after a 'measure' and the end is 'tied'._
Also refers to a situation where an opposition bowler, usually a 'skip' is playing so well that if the home team are holding shot they are inclined to 'tie up' the other skip by his shoelaces to prevent him bowling any more woods.

TRIAL ENDS. _In competitive bowls, each person is usually allowed to bowl two 'trial' woods in each direction as a means of assessing the line and length of the green._
In reality this information is of little value and the phrase relates more to the fact that if the game is lost on the last end the skip is summarily 'tried' by his fellow team members.
This is the nearest to a 'lynch mob' that this game produces.

WATERPROOFS. _Anyone approaching the game with a sensible attitude will realise that sooner or later there will be a tumultuous downpour sometime during their game._
The onset of monsoon-like conditions managing to deposit several inches of rain on the green amid waterspouts and hurricane strength ice-cold winds will quickly remind you of the purchase you should have made.
A good set of waterproofs is essential and should be capable of covering thermal suits, over-trousers, shirts, jumpers, body warmers and jackets in a multitudinous array of protection.
The bowler will now be perfectly dry, warmed like toast and totally snug in his safe haven.
However, his rendition of the 'Michelin Man' will leave him struggling to pick up his wood and incapable of bowling one!

WHITES. _The combination of greys accidentally washed in the domestic bleach, resulting in a good excuse to have an afternoon of gentlemanly bowling with tea and biscuits._

WIND. _Nothing to do with the roughage in a bowlers diet, but a non-governed force of nature capable of creating havoc on a well trimmed bowling green._

WOOD. _The original name for a bowl, but sometimes made with the suggestion that the bowler concerned would be better playing with a No. 2 wood from the local golf club._
There's also nothing more confusing than standing on a green with a bowl in one hand, jack in the other, trying to play against a bowler named Jack Wood! I know. I've met him!

THE PLAYERS

THE CAPTAIN *Apparently related to 'God', also known as 'he who must be obeyed' and 'The 'Commander-in Chief'. Notorious for rallying players more like marshalling a battalion of infantry with rousing speeches, blood stirring battle-cries, 'do or die' firing shots and always being right, of course.*

LEAD *A player whose sole purpose in life is to place bowls near the cot just so other bowlers can take great delight in knocking them off again!*
The role of the 'lead' is vital for anyone wishing to play their game at the peak of perfection, as they will become the best 'drawer' of bowls in the club.
If only they can find a way of keeping them there, they will become champion!

NO.2 *A position playable by any bowler who is able to produce a steady game whilst under the watchful, disparaging glare of their 'skip'.*
They should possess a strong aversion to playing two woods alike as their 'skip' is bound to request a change of their line, length, weight, and shot with every wood.
They are expected to be capable of consolidating the position left by their 'lead' but more often than not are required to rescue a game fast deteriorating, because the lead is still recovering from a stag party the night before.

NO.3 *This 'runner-up' position is reserved for a person who is challenging for the position of 'skip', having learnt all there is to know about running woods and firing, whilst having forgotten the basics of drawing a shot.*
They are a bowler who often states that they have played a 'tactical wood' wherever the bowl finishes!
In reality, they are more often responsible for the construction of a row of bowls similar to the 'Berlin Wall' in front of the head, thus preventing either 'skip' being able to reach, or even see the cot.

SKIP *Usually the largest, strongest man in the club, able to gain tremendous speeds in excess of 100mph when delivering the wood.*

His delivery accompanied by great gusto, impressive shouts, and bursts of energetic running is unfortunately with the accuracy of a blind hedgehog.

The resulting demolition of the ditch wall, or even worse, the neighbouring head is frowned upon and when, occasionally, the correct head is struck the other members of the team can be found taking cover in the nearby rose beds.

SUPPORTER *A keen bowler with some knowledge of the game, having missed their favourite football match, had a lot of beers and in need of someone to laugh at.*

SPECTATOR *A passer by with little knowledge of the game, having missed their favourite football match, had one or two beers and in need of someone to laugh at.*

MARKER *A favourite in the club house; volunteers get the opportunity to stand at the other end of the green and make professional commentary on the game in progress.*

Their speech is usually restricted to "YES", "NO" and "IT'S A MEASURE".

Frustrated bowlers have been known to ignore the cot and bowl at the markers feet when 'playing weight'.

The selected 'marker', a former member of NATO and experienced negotiator of fifteen years should equip himself with the following to ensure fluid flow to the game...

Two measures of which one should be the string variety, both with a non-stretch guarantee certificate as supplied by the Department of Weights and Measures.
A case of soft white chalk and a case of white spray marker.
Score card (in case somebody does actually score!)
Six long-life waterproof ink pens
Red Cross flag of truce and Flare pistol (emergency use only)
Torch (large floodlight variety)
Soft brush (to sweep away leaves, worm casts, etc)
Roll of white tape (to cordon off head whilst measuring)
Whistle or Fog Horn (to restore order in case of riot)
Sandwich box and Thermos flask (optional)
Body/Leg/Shin pads (with Kevlar armour inserts)

UMPIRE *A prestigious position much fancied in bowling, when a selected official gets to spend the day in an armchair, wearing his best blazer, supping tea with biscuits and enjoying the delights of a snooze in the afternoon sun.*

On the rare occasion an umpire is called to the green, it is usually on the pretence of a 'measure' but more the desire of the bowlers to check which flavour sandwiches are tucked away in the umpire's attaché case.

Bets are often passed regarding his ability to arise out of the club armchair after consuming several 'flavoured' coffees and two slices of Mrs Spindleforth's best strawberry gateau.

DR W. G. GRACE TAKES THE FIELD

THE COMPETITIONS

Essentially, in every club there are a variety of
competitions, the mainstays of which are....

SINGLES   One man bands, loners, glory hunters
and 'characters' please apply....

PAIRS   Always handy to have someone else
to blame if you lose....

TRIPLES   The minimum basic number required for a
good argument....

FOURS   All the makings of a full scale riot....

<u>**MIXED COMPETITIONS**</u> Great fun, the men will blame the
women as being incapable of ever reaching the head, whilst
the women will blame the men for being inflexible, single-
minded and sexist....

<u>**COUNTY COMPETITIONS**</u> As above but with a much better
class of argument and much bigger words...

<u>**EBA/EBF COMPETITIONS**</u>   (see tournaments and festivals)
Apart from these 'gold cup' events there will always be a
number of challenge and memorial competitions named after
all and sundry including the green keeper's goldfish and the
Chairman's nephew's grandson's pet dog.
There may also be an introduction of a number of daily leagues
named after events or brands.
Therefore, bulletin boards often carry a request for bowlers to
play in the Football league, Sports Car league, Fish Species
league, Board Games league and Alcoholic Beverages league.
To ensure every bowler gets at least one game there may also
be the introduction of a variety of 'opens' including Handicap,
Amateur, Under 5's, Over 55's and Captain's 'best mates' Cup.

ETIQUETTE~EBF BOWLS TOURNAMENT

There are a number of rules and regulations laid down for bowling competitions. Here are a number of such instances taken directly from EBF Tournament reference books and a number of alternative 'tongue in cheek' interpretations

NO TRIAL ENDS
Give us one good reason why we should give you a head start? There's a large crowd here today under the assumption that anyone playing in an 'open' tournament must be a member of the National team.
They will have much more to gossip about if you all play badly for the first few ends.
Besides, if you have a trial end you'll discover we haven't cut the grass for two weeks and we have watered it every night. It's much more fun watching your wood struggling to get half way up the green...

NO VISITING THE HEAD IN ANY COMPETITION
You definitely have no chance to walk up and see where your woods are, you'll just have to play by guesswork and memory. There is a guy on the roof with a walkie-talkie and a telescope who will be glad to give you a few tips as long as you slip us £20.
No visiting the other 'head' either; you'll just have to cross your legs tightly, which will make for some interesting deliveries....

ALL SINGLES GAMES, 21 SHOTS UP
Nice and simple, the first one to score twenty-one shots wins. Oh by the way, did we tell you it's only one wood per bowler and every time you lose an end you have one point deducted from your score.
Hope you brought a packed lunch and haven't booked your evening meal?

PAIRS/TRIPLES 21 LIVE ENDS OR 1HR 15 MINUTES FOR ALL ROUNDS UP TO THE SEMIS.

Let's face it, you have absolutely no hope of playing a full twenty-one ends of pairs or triples in ninety minutes, there's more chance of a snowball getting a suntan!

Concentrate of getting an early lead and play for time.

At 1 hour 14 minutes 45 seconds, if you are tied at 10 shots each and your partner is dithering on the mat with the last bowl, just remember it'll take 15 seconds for his wood to get to the head.

Perhaps you have some encouraging words for him that'll make him bowl quickly???

NO JACK CAST AFTER 1 HR 10 MINS

Watch the game at the 1hr 9 minute marker for some great entertainment.

Where any teams are slightly ahead and they are ready to deliver the cot, the 'lead' will adopt all manner of 'sporting' tactics to hold on to the cot until the final whistle.

There will be sudden outbreaks of cramp, seizure, muscle damage, ripped trousers, broken shoelaces, dropped woods, and time-consuming corrections to the mat.

The 'lead' may decide to enter into a lengthy debate with the skip, who has suddenly gone deaf, leading to a situation of near riot by the opposing team.

SEMIS/FINALS NO TIME LIMIT 21 LIVE ENDS

Without any time limit, this thoroughly entertaining game will keep the bowling fans amused for hours, if not days.

Without the need to rush, the skip will opt to fire and destroy the entire head whenever his team are more than one shot down. It is recommended that all spectators invest in sleeping bags, thermos flask, and torch for extended evening activities.

Indeed, spectators may be asked to adopt the fashion of a Barry Manilow concert by lining the green with raised lighters at night so the bowlers can see what they're doing.

Often the onset of night can lead to a sudden demise in the game as the shortsighted 'skip' fires and manages to 'take out' a confused glow-worm or cigarette butt instead of the cot.

DEFINITION OF CASTING THE JACK

"The mat should be in place and the jack should be on its way up the rink"

Any 'lead' feeling mischievous will choose to take the ruling literally and walk up the green with the cot in their hand and tongue in cheek. Alternatively, ensuing chaos is usually caused by the mat being placed on the nearby beach or the cot cast up the rinks corner to corner.

If on any end of a game an illegal jack is cast, to save time the following will apply:-

i. The cot will be replaced with a golf ball for the duration of the match as a penalty.
ii. Jack will be asked to produce his birth certificate.
iii. On repetition of the offence, a green coloured golf ball will be used for the duration.
iv. Jack will be paid compensation for injuries received.

If the jack is knocked 'out of rink' the end is deemed to be a no-score dead end and is not to be replayed.

A rule guaranteed to ensure you will not lose the match. Simply hit the cot hard every end knocking it out of rink and the end will have to be replayed. The only snag is that you'll never win the game either and the organising officials may be slightly un-amused if the match is tied at nil – nil after 72 attempted ends.

AND FINALLY

"The organising officials decision is final"

Always be sure you know the Umpires wife, his first name, favourite drink, children's birth-date(s) and best bowling performance. These could be critical in a 'tied end'. In the knowledge that the Umpire is a retired butcher, you can be assured that any arguing with the match official will result in your bowls being placed in the nearest meat mincer and ground into gravy salt.

All competitors to be at the green 15 minutes before the time programmed for their game or, if alternative times are mentioned, 15 minutes before the earliest time

All match times may be subject to alteration without warning and bowlers will not be informed. All new times will be posted 90 seconds before the original start time. At this point 50% of the competitors will discover they have missed their start time and the match is therefore conceded. The remaining 50% will find that their games are postponed to the following day, having driven 250 miles to attend today's game. The ensuing mayhem will be broadcast live to the watching spectators as the officials have failed to turn off the microphone on the main desk.

"The organising officials have the right to take any action deemed necessary to keep the tournament on schedule"

The subsequent actions have been deemed necessary in case of the following delays...

i)   HEAVY RAIN
Wellington boots will be made freely available, as will flotation belts for cots and bowls. In the event of flooded greens, the Umpire will distribute frogman kits and naval compasses. Distress flares are optional.

ii)   SLOW PLAY
Players will be placed in the 'cage of shame' and suspended over the spectators seats for a period of not less than four hours.

iii)   GAME OVER-RUNNING ALLOTTED TIME
The game will be decided by a 'sudden death' hamburger eating competition.

iv)   A MEASURE FOR SHOT
The umpire will call an 'instant' decision based on the view from his telescope by the club bar.

v)   DISPUTE OVER COT LENGTH
The umpire will kick the cot in a direction of his choice

ETIQUETTE:- EBA BOWLS FESTIVAL

There are a number of rules and regulations laid down for bowling competitions. Here are a number of such instances taken directly from EBA festival reference books with alternative 'tongue in cheek' interpretations

PLEASE DO NOT WALK 'SIX ABREAST' DOWN THE ADJOINING RINK

1. *If you walk down the adjoining rink, there is a likelihood of damage to your ankles resulting from obstruction to delivery of bowls, as you will be on the wrong rink.*

2. *Six people together in a line might be misconstrued as a chorus line from 'THE SOUND OF MUSIC'.*

3. *You are on the end rink and could impale yourself on the surrounding fence.*

4. *It is very difficult for six people to agree to do the same thing on a bowling green, even less likely on one rink.*

5) *The local champion racehorse aptly named 'six abreast' is likely to get very excited and deposit a number of unwanted 'sculptures' on the green.*

PLEASE KEEP STILL AT THE END OF THE RINK WHEN A BOWLER IS ABOUT TO PLAY

When a bowler is about to play it is frowned upon if other members dress up in 'clowns' outfits, juggle cots, spin 'woods' on their fingers and participate in other foolish carry-ons for the purpose of entertaining the watching public.
Other, 'non-participating' bowlers should remain firmly rooted to the spot, lower their heart rates to less than 50 beats per minute, ignore infectious itches and resist all temptation to burst into hysterical laughter just as the bowler on the mat is about to deliver his wood.

PLEASE DO NOT WALK AROUND THE SIDES
WHEN PEOPLE ARE ABOUT TO BOWL

It is especially distracting to any bowler mentally preparing to 'deliver his wood' when he notices movement out of the corner of his eye.

If this movement is from the remaining five members of the teams anxious to get to the other end it gives the impression that they have already discounted the impact of the wood about to be bowled. Suitably downhearted the bowler will try to refocus, fail miserably, and turn around angrily to the guilty parties.

At this point, he will foolishly realise that they are in fact the competition Captain and Umpire trying to point out to him that he is in fact bowling on the wrong green, or, worse still, that the game did actually finish on the last end and he doesn't have to bowl!

NO MOBILE PHONES ALLOWED ON THE GREEN

An obvious, although understated fact, everyone is very much aware that mobile phones can NOT bowl!!!

PLEASE DO NOT LEAVE DEAD WOODS
ON THE ADJOINING RINK

Action must be taken to immediately rectify this potentially dangerous situation of impeding the play on the next rink.

Take the following steps immediately.

1) Kick the wood hard to check if it is in fact dead.

2) If the bowl moves, immediately discharge both barrels of a 12 bore shotgun in the general direction of the wood.

The ensuing massacre of the local worm population may be noted and recorded by the watching Greenpeace official.

The owner of the wood is probably slightly concerned about the ensuing 'Swiss cheese' replication of his favourite wood.

To ensure all is as it should be repeat step 1 until it is safe to remove the wood.

PLEASE DO NOT TALK BEHIND THE MAT
WHEN PLAYERS ARE ABOUT TO BOWL

Players often feel the need to discuss, in hushed tones, the potential outcome of the forthcoming shot, also the wide-ranging options and tactics for their own next wood.

This can be acceptable if it is done in such a way as not to distract, annoy, or irritate the bowler.

It is not acceptable to make derisory comments about his wife/girlfriend through a power megaphone at 112 decibels just eight inches away from his right ear as he attempts to bowl.

Nor is it appropriate to debate the outcome of the next general election, council tax rises, Mrs Puddingmoor's young daughter, or the increase of alcohol prices at the local supermarket.

PLEASE DO NOT CROWD AROUND WHEN
MEASURING IS TAKING PLACE.

Alarm was registered by bowlers on reading this ruling as no definition was given as to exactly what was to be measured!

There was some apparent concern that certain measurements would indeed attract a crowd!!

It was decided, that in these circumstances the opposing bowling teams would form a 'scrum' around the cot and the umpire would be 'injected' into the surrounded head much like the delivery of a rugby ball.

SKIPS AND NO.3'S SHOULD NOT HOLD UNECESSARILY
LONG CONVERSATIONS WHILE CHANGING ENDS
HALFWAY DOWN THE GREEN

Whilst 'skips' and team members usually pause to discuss tactics and possible shots into the 'head' the umpires do frown upon lengthy discussions into such less important issues such as literary comparisons of the entire works of William Shakespeare.

Team members are more likely to be confused by the request to 'change ends' halfway down the green.

Many 'leads' have since taken to placing the mat half way up the green to save on time.

**DAMAGE TO THE GREEN IS CAUSED BY
INCORRECT DELIVERY TO THE HEAD, IF YOU
HAVE A PROBLEM WITH YOUR DELIVERY OUR
COACHES WILL BE PLEASED TO HELP**

*Possibly the most amusing, theoretically rhetorical,
innuendo-based, ruling I have seen so far.........*

We must assume one of the following

i) *This is a ruling for any amateur or semi-pro boxer
who, without the use of a set of professional gloves
to hand, has taken to striking the surface of the
green with his opponents head.*

ii) *This is a low-key advertising campaign for the local
'gender' therapy clinic with use of subtle 'Freudian'
double-meanings and innocent innuendo.*

iii) *This is an offer of professional help by experienced
coach drivers to transport your team and luggage or
to assist you with the redistribution of your postal
service deliveries.*

iv) *Possibly, losing bowlers, in desperation have taken
to bowling over-arm?*

v) *Professional players are available to step in as
'substitutes' if you prefer to fake a sporting injury?*

vi) *It is strongly recommended that your bowl not be
discharged from the local seafront cannon when
'firing' at the head!*

vii) *A professional bowler will assist you in practicing
your delivery without any fear of damage to the
bowling surface. Please follow him to the beach
immediately!*

viii) *Having failed to learn how to 'draw' a wood it is not
advisable to paste a first class stamp on your bowl
and pop it in a mailbox. True, the wood will arrive on
time, in fact quicker than your current delivery
speed; it will also be delivered to the correct head!
However, the courier van is likely to make quite a
mess of the bowling surface and your game may
literally become stuck in a rut!*

BOWLING SHOTS

BLOCK Once a team hold a strong position in the head they may opt to protect that head by placing a wood or 'blocker' directly in the drawing line of the oppositions next intended wood. Depending on the width of that 'line', the bowler may choose to bowl several blockers or perhaps even bowl his bowling bag with his woods in it! Last-ditch desperate attempts to save the shot may include the team skip falling down in front of the head just before the opposition's last wood arrives.

DITCHER You anticipate using the 4kg 'cannon-ball' in your hand to hit the two and a half inch wide white ball lying eighty feet away. You envisage your wood sticking to it like glue and placing it in the ditch alongside your wood after failing to 'draw' with your first three bowls. The team, anticipating your actions, have taken refuge in the clubhouse.

DRAW The bowlers much sought after 'Holy Grail', mythically resulting in the anointment of the wood with a white stick. In reality, there is greater probability of drawing the shot by use of a pencil and paper. Beware of any 'lead' wearing a Stetson, it's probably some escapee from a line dance known as 'quick on the draw two-gun McGraw'.

FIRING SHOT Similar to a 'tactical wood' played with great exuberance and plenty of weight, often resembling a large nuclear device on the rare occasion it actually hits the head. The usual outcome is that, having cleared half of the woods from the green you gain a 'wick', four 'lucky rubs', a 'fluke' and a 'trail' to end up in the ditch 'touching the cot' with your nearest opponents woods on the next rink, all this after they had drawn four perfect woods to the cot.

FLUKE Usually the combination of a 'wick shot' and a 'firing wood', diverting through the head like a runaway express train, removing, simultaneously the shot wood, and trailing the cot for shot.

FULL LENGTH *The placing of the cot at such a long distance that the umpire or a 'spotter' is called on to the green with a telescope to relay fall of shot to the bowler.*

LUCKY RUB *Similar to a 'fluke' but with the added influence of a bowler 'rubbing' his lucky mascot (a gift from Mystic Meg!) before bowling his wood. Bowlers have experienced disastrous last ends by accidentally rubbing the wood and bowling the mascot.*

REST *The use of an opponent's wood as a ledge or rest on which to stop, thereby becoming the shot wood in its place. More likely to be an indication of an under-bowled wood stopping half way up the green, thereby 'having a rest' before being promoted up the green.*

RUNNING WOOD *A great excuse for any wood that passes the cot at speeds in excess of 40mph desperately seeking the 'little white thing' which is quite safe, as usual, being several metres away from the head of bowls anyway.*

SHORT LENGTH *The placing of the cot at such a short distance to the mat that the bowler actually steps over the cot to deliver his wood.*

TAP'N'LIE *Nothing to do with plumbing, the effect of tapping out an opponents wood and lying where it once sat, more often the result of obtaining more touches from preceding woods than a pinball on a bagatelle board.*

TACTICAL WOOD *Usually a name given to any bowl that completely misses the head by several metres, but may have a million to one chance of becoming shot wood one day.*

TOUCHER *With a helping hand from lumps, bumps, wind-factor, worm casts and an element of luck you have picked up the cot with your last wood, tucking it away behind the previous six woods and turned 'three down' and 'game against' into 'holding shot'. The opponent now needs a radar to see the exact position of the cot and may resort to bribery, hair pulling and fits of manic depression, often interspersed with frustrated repetitive calls of 'I DON'T BELIEVE IT" amidst other ramblings, mutterings and polishing of woods.*

TRAIL *A smart term for picking up the cot and moving it from your opponent's woods to your own. In reality the combination of a 'running wood' and a 'fluke', picking up the cot to take it a further ten feet to your three previous woods which were all too heavy and over-ran as well.*

WICK *A desperate shot usually requiring the combination of a wood played 'too heavy' and 'too wide' coming into contact with a number of other woods en-route which divert it towards the cot. Often, rubbing salt into the wound, the bowl becomes a 'chalker' as well, at which the bowler may look smug and deserving of a pat on the back for calculating a directional formula greater than that of Einstein's 'theory of relativity'.*

YARD ON *Effectively a good excuse to play a slightly heavier wood too tight on the pretext of drawing, and then, if resulting in a successful alteration to the head, proudly stating that you played 'a yard on' to dislodge the shot wood and 'got the right result'.*

THE WOODEN SPOON

The scourge of every bowling captain and club touring competition side. This 'larger than life' award is reserved as a public humiliation for the team of players performing least well, or who, to put it politely, were rubbish!!! Should you be so unlucky as to be in this team, be prepared for a ritual presentation in front of the entire bowling club, County representatives, local press and associated family and friends. The 'award' may be subsequently displayed over the club bar for a period of not less than twelve months to ensure every member of every visiting club is aware of your humiliation.

GLOSSARY OF BOWLING COMMENTS

You stand on the green and play your wood. You have given it your best shot, played with the combination of your experience, knowledge and confidence. Your trusting partner stands at the other end with a forced smile and makes a modest comment reflecting on your play. Now here's your chance to find out the real truth behind their comments and discover what they are thinking!!!

"BRILLIANT!"
"Hold the press! Wow! Amazing! You finally did it!
After four months, thirteen days, you played the perfect drawing wood, a 'chalker', and trailed the cot for four shots. They have one more wood left so tie their shoe laces together whilst I lie down in front of the head."

"CHANGE THE LENGTH"
"You can't reach a long cot, you're two metres away. You can't bowl to a short cot, you're two metres through the head. Anywhere in the middle and you go to pieces and end up on the next rink. How about we start with a two metre cast and work up from there?"

"DITCH THE COT!"
"There's more wood in front of the cot then there is in a B & Q timber yard, we're six down, but we do have a back wood six metres away at the edge of the green."

"FIRE!!!"
"OH MY GOD WE'RE 8 SHOTS DOWN, THIS IS YOUR LAST ATTEMPT, THERE'S NOTHING WITHIN TEN FEET AND WE'RE DESPERATE!!!"

"GIVE IT MORE GREEN"
"You may have noticed that you're not holding shot? You may have even noticed that you don't have a wood on the same green? Could the reason be that you're bowling just a bit too tight and by the time the bowl leaves your hand it's already actually missed the cot?"

"GOOD TRY"

"You did it again!! That's the third time you have drawn shot wood to the 'pigeon droppings' which are actually six feet away from the cot you're supposedly aiming for. Perhaps you should try bowling with your eyes open this time and look at the right rink?"

"HARD LUCK"

"Well partner that was truly a touch of bad luck and you have my heart-felt sympathy. After all, when you released that bowl with power, weight, and loss of line, who was to know that it would career through the clubhouse in such a way? After, getting a wick off the Umpires chair and cannoning off the bar stools you retrieved the situation with a brilliant escape through the Fire Exit. Who would have anticipated that, after hitting the ditch-work, rocketing a full six feet into the air and rolling up the green, your bowl would end up just two inches short of being shot wood?"

"HOW GOOD IS YOUR MEMORY?"

"You haven't got a hope of drawing another wood to the cot it's taken you fifteen ends and sixty one attempts to get this one."

"I DON'T BELIEVE IT"

"I am truly lost for words; I simply do not believe it. I watched your delivery with a mixture of nervous trepidation and unwarranted fear. You delivered the wood almost perfectly in a near flawless display of exhibition bowling. There you are in all your glory, proud of your efforts, holding shot wood, just two inches away from the cot on Rink 7. Meanwhile back here on Rink 1 we were just wondering if perhaps you'd like to face the right way next time?"

"I DON'T THINK ITS THERE?" (Bowler)

"Excuse me skip, bowling partner, true friend and patient teacher, I think it fair to give you advance notice and fair warning that the wood I have just bowled is sadly lacking in weight. In fact, on reflection, I can safely and truly say that it really hasn't got a hope of even reaching the half way mark!"

"I'M SORRY ABOUT THAT"

"We're not sorry at all, your lucky wick just removed the opposition's three perfectly drawn woods from the cot, and they are now 'one down'."

"I THINK IT'S A MEASURE"

"We are at least two shots down but my glass eye and shaky hands will ensure that my 'elastic' measure gives us a fighting chance of holding the shot!"

"IT'S A BIT THIN" (Bowler)

"Oh dear, I can see I've bowled that one so tight that I'll probably end up with a 'toucher' on the rink marker. I had better warn my skip before he says something irrational and rude. Perhaps he'll look on the bright side, after all, that is the closest wood I've bowled tonight?"

"IT'S THE LITTLE WHITE THING"

"For twenty years, on every end of every game after every wood you have to ask me where the cot is?
My patience is wearing a bit thin, would you like me to paint it day-glo pink, or shall I photograph the head and e-mail you with my mobile phone?"

"JUST A DRAW"

"You're supposed to be drawing to the little white thing, not killing wildlife in the hedgerow, your last wood got a speeding ticket!!"

"JUST THROUGH THE HEAD"

"Ok, I accept you had a heavy night and you still can't see the head, but it would be nice if you could bowl at least one wood within 6 feet of the cot."

"JUST RUNNING A LITTLE"

"I can see that you are bowling fractionally heavy, shall I go and wait on the other side of the ditch to collect it, or will I need to get my car keys first so I at least have an even chance of catching up with it?"

"LETS HAVE A CHANGE AROUND"

"I'll come down there and bowl your woods as 'lead', then I'll play my own woods as 'skip' whilst you go and make the tea. At least that way we'll have some chance of not being four down every time I normally pick up my first wood."

"LOVELY WEIGHT"

"Congratulations, well done, magnificent effort partner, absolutely perfect weight, your wood is only four inches from the cot. Unfortunately that cot is on Rink 6 and we are playing on Rink 5!"

"NEVER MIND"

"Give up now, go back to the bar and order me a strong double, you really couldn't hit a barn door with a cannon ball. With two metres to draw in you still end up with shot wood on the next rink, two in the ditch and one closer to you than the cot!"

"PLAY WEIGHT"

"You can't draw to save your life, you're always heavy! Play your normal shot and we'll simply pretend you were playing a tactical wood."

"RUN IT OUT"

"Your wood is actually never going to reach the head, but it'll make you feel a lot better if you actually think it ever had a fighting chance of making a difference."

"SAME AGAIN!"

"Oh well, we've had three wicks in a row, do what you normally do and lets pretend we're actually playing for it!!"

"THAT'S A BIT OF A WOBBLER"

"Ok, it's like this, when you bowl the wood you are supposed to have the narrow bit resting in the palm of your hand with your fingers on the grip. From that last delivery I can deduce that the wood was resting on its sticker and you obviously have no idea how to play the game?"

"THAT LOOKS A BIT HEAVY"

"Don't worry partner, you keep putting your woods in the rose bed, at least they're safe in there. But you might want to consider donating a few pounds to the slightly upset green keeper who's currently advancing on your position with a large spade in his hand."

"THAT'S FURTHER THAN I GO ON HOLIDAY"

"You can take this two ways partner. On the assumption that I regularly go to Florida for my holidays you are virtually assured that I am singularly unimpressed by your pathetic attempt at placing a short cot. Would you like me to go and retrieve it off the next green so you can have another go?"

"TIME FOR A TEA BREAK"

"We are thirty two shots behind after ten ends, let's take a break and pray for a heavy downpour or perhaps slip some sleeping tablets into the opponents' tea."

"TRY THE OTHER HAND"

"Well let's face it, the way you're bowling on your current hand you might as well bowl with your foot. You'll never draw the shot on that side and I have more confidence of the TITANIC avoiding the iceberg than you hitting the target on this hand."

"UNLUCKY"

"Your over-weight and tight wood has careered across the head clipping the cot sideways from our teams 'shot wood' towards the opponent's woods who now hold five shots. The 250 members watching the game are probably not saying very nice things about you right at this minute!!"

"VISIT THE HEAD"

"Come up here and have a look at how bad you're really playing and then go and hide in the toilet for fifteen minutes, maybe the opposition will go off the boil."

"WELL BOWLED PARTNER"

"You may have guessed that, by the way I've taken off my watch and have now retrieved the club calendar that I am going to say something facetious. Ah, yes! Here we are! July 11th 2.30pm, four years ago, gosh what a day that was. I am sure you remember it well, after all that was the last time you actually bowled a 'toucher'!!"

"WE'RE HOLDING SHOT"

"I'd truly like to say well done partner for bowling a superb wood, a perfect draw beating all other woods with a mixture of quality, class and true distinction. In reality the only reason we're holding shot is that you bowled first and you've bowled the only wood so far!"

"WE'RE SIX DOWN (AGAIN)"

"You couldn't hit a barn door three feet away, give up, go home, get drunk, pack away your bowls, and take up something safe like dominoes or chess."

"WHAT DO YOU THINK?" (Bowler)

"Don't ask me I'm just the skip, my mind is too numb to register the unique style of your bowling. How can I be expected to read a head when I can't even work out what you'll do with your woods next?"

"WHERE'S THE JACK?" (Bowler)
"Apart from the obvious, tedious, and stupid reply of 'up this end' I can now only estimate its approximate position given its last known speed, trajectory, and angle of ascent after your last wood hit it!"

"WHO'S HOLDING SHOT"
"Is this 'groundhog day' or are you just being this stupid to annoy me? You have just visited the head, only four woods have been bowled, and you can clearly see the cot. As you have yet to bowl your wood I think we can safely assume that very little has changed!"

"YOU ARE TIGHTER THAN A KIPPERS LIP"
"Apart from the insinuation that your late father was a salty old sea dog and with no inference to the fact you are probably so inebriated that you can not even see the head. Have you even tried to find a kippers lip? Well on the assumption that you would even be daft enough to try, take my word for it that your bowling is as bad as your fishing and you definitely can't fish!"

"YOU'LL NEED TO TAKE A TRAIN TO REACH THAT ONE"
"The old ones are always the best aren't they? Basically, you are at one end of the green, I'm up here at the far end of the green with the cot. It's the 1st of May, it's raining, the grass is long, the ground soft, you haven't bowled for two years and you're asking me how you should play your wood???"

Playing of matches at night with luminous bowls was not a great success. However, the new all black leisure bowling outfits proved to be very popular.

GREEN KEEPERS GUIDE

BOWLING SURFACE

This much loved and nurtured piece of 'old England' has heraldic links dating back hundreds of years.

Long term and dedicated research by the green keeper's wife has probably discovered that the legendary Sir Francis Drake once played an end of bowls on this hallowed turf.

The manicured surface has been hand trimmed with nail scissors, each blade swept into place with a soft comb, and all markers polished until they dazzle in the morning sun.

Make no mistake, any bowler, from 'absolute novice' to England champion takes their own life in their hands if they so much as 'bounce' a wood or damage a single blade!

CAR PARK

In the halcyon days before the invention of cars green keepers used to keep bales of straw in pastured areas to cater for the equestrian who always choose to ride to the bowling green on a Sunday morning.

Depending on their position within the club their faithful steed would range from a thoroughbred racehorse to a tatty mule.

The keeper was always on hand with his trusted bucket and shovel on the off chance he was able to acquire some well nurtured natural manure for his prize rose beds.

Nowadays he grudgingly watches on as an endless procession of four-wheel drive vehicles turn his carefully swept parking space into an army assault range.

Take careful note that the President's and Chairman's reserved spaces have their own individual flower beds, potted plants and neatly presented gravelled areas, whilst the lesser mortals make do with a shabby dustbin and an assortment of pebbles from the local beach.

CROSS CUTTING

This is the time-honoured tradition of cutting the green 'from corner to corner' eventually producing a fine textured pattern and an even roll to the bowling green.

The keeper, in passing the time of day deep in thought, has been known to lose track of his locality and, in failing to turn in time, cross-cut the ditch embankment, flowerbed and Captain's blazer resting on the grass verge.

Members will soon note that there are times when the green keeper is not to be disturbed and they would be better off leaping into an active volcano rather than face his wrath.

Such an indication is given when the green keeper prepares his cutting tools halfway through the afternoon match and proceeds to cut the grass even whilst play in still underway.

Be assured that he will NOT, under any circumstances, deviate from his 'straight line'.

Any wood or cot that happens to lie in his path is best removed or face the prospect of having several new 'grip' marks etched into it by the 'diamond edged' mower blades.

Firing woods already played that happen to come into contact with the moving machinery will discover that the mower's sides carry more armour plating than a world war two battleship.

A dustpan and brush is made available for the hapless bowler to sweep up the remains of his bowl afterwards.

CUP MUSHROOMS

Early risers' en-route for their daily walk along the beach, passing the clubhouse, may notice a crouched form hurriedly scampering around the green.

Be aware, this is not an indiscrete angler hastily removing large quantities of fresh worms for his days fishing; it is in fact the green keeper harvesting his latest crop of recently sown mushrooms which he has been 'passing off' as fairy rings.

Early indication of a forthcoming crop is a sudden lack of interest in cutting the grass over a 72-hour period.

FLAIL

There is some hushed whispering in darkened corners of the clubhouse that the green keeper, in his ancestry was formerly a custodian of a medieval castle dungeon.

Early in the morning, during the Summer season, especially after the nights dew has raised a large number of 'worm casts' he is to be seen marching on to the grass with a large, javelin-like pole in his hand.

This 'device' when opened produces a 'whip-like' flail capable of decimating huge areas with a single stroke and beheading hundreds of worms, beetles and 'daddy long-legs'.

Numerous species are now on the 'endangered species' list.

Police are currently investigating an unconfirmed report regarding the discovery of a Hessian sack full of small 'dolls' dressed in miniature bowling outfits, along with a large number of ladies hatpins!!.

LOPPERS

With the usual boundaries of ancient hedgerow, mature trees and more recently planted conifer trees towering high into the heavens, the green keeper's ever growing repertoire of weaponry has recently increased with the' LOPPER'.

From a hand held telescopic pole the keeper never fails to hold his audience enthralled as he produces length after extendable length until his pole spirals into the higher branches some 70ft in the air.

The audience hold their breath as the guide rope is tugged and the titanium edged lopper blades bite into the chosen branch.

Somewhere above an ear-splitting 'crack' like an African thunderstorm announces the pending arrival of an untamed, 'out-of-control' branch falling earthward.

This 500kg, 28ft monster plunges to the ground denuding all the trees of their leafy foliage within a ten-metre radius.

The astonished, awe-struck bowlers, peering from behind the clubhouse, are often momentarily 'blinded' as the full force of the blazing sun blasts through the suddenly exposed gap in the tree-line.

MOLES
Devious near sighted, night-time tunnel excavators who's sole ambition in life is to break through the multi-layered defence line of deep planted wire netting, concrete ditches, sensitised 'hot wired' cattle prods and passive minefields that surround the finest wormery in Gt. Britain.

As of yet no breakthrough in peace negotiations have been reported, although the United Nations are looking at leaked documents indicating large quantities of chemical weapons recently purchased in the middle east by a Mr G. Keeper?

MOSS
Viewed by most keepers as an alien disease inflicted on the world by a passing ancient meteorite thousands of years ago.

They will spend days scrutinising every square inch of the green with a magnifying glass more powerful than Jodrell Bank.

In the unlikely event that a microscopic spore is discovered the keeper is likely to summon an ecological 'swat team' to terminate all life in a five metre radius.

Hence, at last, an explanation to the development of large brown patches on bowling greens.

MOWER
Essentially a state-of the art machine for cutting grass in precise, equal and level lengths, complete with hydraulic-sprung heated drivers seat, ten speed gear box, air-conditioned cabin, mini-bar, microwave and pot-noodle rack.

Unfortunately, due to falling club finances, this year the keeper has to make do with an 18th century, hand held, cylinder drum cutter which couldn't shave the frost off a fridge door.

SECATEURS
Miniature, hand-held, versions of those 'loppers'.
These 'harmless' devices are capable of coppicing stems up to four inches in diameter given the pressure that the well-seasoned green keepers hands can apply.

Members should also note that brake pipes, exhaust pipes and throttle cables are equally accessible targets should they upset the keeper before the end of a match.

ON RINK / OFF RINK

Bowling rinks are traditionally played in measured widths and set places on a rotating basis North-South or East-West in order to spread out the 'wear and tear' on the green into measured evenness.

However, on the eve of any club competition the green keeper, in a mad fit of over-zealousness will reduce the 8 rink green to a 6 rink green, spreading the remaining rinks out from a centre point so that the bowlers are now bowling on grass they were previously walking up and down on the preceding day.

The ensuing 'loss of line' caused by the influences of footprints, flattened grass, bounced woods and wet worm casts brings the game into total disarray.

With bowling reduced to the level of 'beginners luck' the last end is normally the one that counts and the scorecard will reflect some wild scoring including a count of sixteen on one end because half the woods from the next rink were in the wrong 'head'.

PIGEONS

Second on any green keeper's 'hit list', just behind 'moss' lays the old-fashioned Wood Pigeon.

These lovable, cute, feathered friends are a popular delight on the ladies bird table with their gentle 'cooing' and preening.

The green keeper has a somewhat different outlook regarding these 'overstuffed turkeys on matchsticks'.

Always to be found at the top of the nearby conifers just prior to any match, the keeper knows that, as soon as his back is turned, they will gently swoop across his prized green splattering it with a vast array of 'droppings'

The aforementioned green now looking like it has been 'three rounds in a paintball game', is instantly subjected to a full pressure wash by the panic-stricken green keeper.

Members turning up for a match fifteen minutes later, at the end of a hot summers day, can't understand why there is a duck pond in the middle of the green and are startled by the subsequent 'subsidence' as the mat they are standing on sinks slowly into the wet turf.

RAMP

A large, portable, rectangular sheet of 10mm exterior plywood rescued from the inner roof of the old clubhouse; This is provisionally reserved by the green keeper for machinery access to the green from the surrounding embankment.

However, there have been a number of reported occasions when the keeper, a former skateboard fanatic, has been seen performing aerial stunts with the large mower.

On reaching the longest 'cut' on the green, normally corner to corner, he accelerates rapidly through the ten gears to a mind-numbing speed of 13mph.

Upon reaching the ramp and using left brake only, he is able to execute a 360-degree turn on the front roller whilst doing a handstand on the steering column.

ROSE BED

Amid the carefully cultivated flower beds surrounding the club green, in the centre of perfumed petunias, cornflowers, sweet peas and geraniums, stands the green keeper's prize rose bed.

His treasured centrepiece, a large bloomed pale lemon variety of 'Molly Coddle III', a selective variety hard grafted onto a thousand year old ancient stem.

Named after the love of his life, he tenderly cares for the rose with copious quantities of local manure, fresh spring water, and a veritable assault pack of ant, aphid, and anti fungal-rot sprays.

A bowler takes his own life in his hands should he make indiscrete or flippant remarks regarding Molly Coddle III.

It is often noted that panic stricken skips, forced to 'fire' at a 'head' near the aforementioned rose bed often have their car engine started and the door open, just in case any bowl should leave the green and head in the general direction of the treasured rose.

ROLLER

Any person who has seen the film 'NEVER ENDING STORY' will understand the comparison between the green keeper with his roller and the film character 'The Rock Biter'.

Generally, a passive, peaceful, easy-going, and friendly figure, all changes once behind the steering column of 'The Roller'.

This five tonne monstrosity rising by its oak/iron handle fully eight feet off the ground is a sight to behold.

Even more so when the keeper rolls it, puffing and panting with exertion, to the edge of the ramp.

The roller, on gaining inertia and velocity as it trundles down the severely stressed ramp, accelerates away across the green with the keeper hanging on for dear life, his body extending horizontally from the handles like a wind-sock in a hurricane.

It has been known to take up to fifteen club members to extricate the roller from the far ditch wall and several stiff brandies to remove the keeper's fingers from the handle.

SCARIFY

The art of careful management of the green allowing the keeper to thin out the grass, or increase its breathing and thus its saturation point, making for improved playability.

On one end of a scale, subtle, even 'spiking' of the green, on the other, the removal of vast numbers of deep circular cores.

Both are delicate operations requiring a high degree of professional knowledge and experience.

Imagine the image of 'THE ROLLER' as described earlier, add a multitude of large spikes to the main drum, now resembling a portable portcullis, add an even more nervous green keeper, introduce inertia and run for cover!

SPIDER

One of the highlights of every 'open' day or touring event, a special mention then for the bowler's favourite, the 'spider'.

This sporting ritual is every journalists delight and a green keeper's worst nightmare!

Take fifty bowlers, give them each a single wood, and ask them to space themselves out along the four edges of the green.

At this point, the green is likely to develop a pronounced hump in the centre due to the combined weight distributed around its perimeter, in fact it may be eligible for crown green games.

The keeper by this time has pulled out the remains of his greying hair as he surveys the collateral damage to the carefully manicured edges of the green which now simultaneously support 50 pairs of finely balanced feet

A cot is placed in the centre of the green and, on the blow of a whistle, every bowler, as one body, releases their bowls with the intent of being the nearest bowl to the cot!

As fifty woods collide, the cot is usually re-located to the other side of the village and a cloud of chalk dust rises like a Saharan sandstorm.

The bald, hysterical, dust covered and shell-shocked green keeper sitting astride his roller bears an uncanny resemblance to Rommel at this stage.

As the dust settles, the woods are seen piled in the centre much like a stack of profiteroles and the keeper has to be visibly restrained from scaling their summit with the club flag.

TRIMMERS
A veritable ironmongery with a selection of different sized 'custom built' and 'off the shelf' cutters.

These may range from large, long handled, spring loaded shafts capable of exerting 4 tonnes of pressure P.S.I. to platinum-coated edge cutters guaranteed to within 1/1000th of an inch.

Tweezer-like manicure scissors for trimming individual blades of grass are essential for the finishing touches.

TURF DRESSING
Not as you imagine an extremely large Elastoplast to protect the damaged green, more an environmentally friendly powdered fertilizer scattered evenly over the ravaged green to encourage and stimulate grass reproduction

The keeper zealously guards his prized stock of pre-Victorian compost much like Long John Silver with his pirate's chest on Treasure Island.

Anyone coming into contact with this 'soil enhancer' should seek medical assistance immediately as the sulphur and phosphorous-based mix is actually taken from a pre-war recipe for Mustard Gas.

WORMS

An army of wriggling creatures who have developed and matured over many years of nurturing greens and gardens.

The natural defence mechanism of these harmless creatures has learned to restore amputated body parts, growing a head at each end and 'giving life' to every dissected section as a means of protecting themselves against the wicked 'green keeper'.

In his innocence, the keeper, with flail in hand, has managed to produce the largest population of 2" long worms within a given density anywhere in the UK.

The 500,000 strong army of wriggly midgets wait for the onset of a wild wet night just prior to any major competition in which to run riot and reduce the proud green to a landscape simulating a Himalayan mountain range.

SHED

A dilapidated, weather worn, wooden shack that stands alone in the distant corner of the club property, usually hidden by an array of unmanaged and 'out of control' shrubbery.

Festooned in Ivy, Virginia Creeper, Clematis and rampant Russian Vine here stands the green keeper's 'castle'.

Even club Presidents are required to give three weeks notice in writing prior to any visit to this legendary domain.

Inside, amid old newspapers, carpet cut-offs and an array of ancient gardening paraphernalia lays an impressive array of well oiled, gleaming, and razor sharp cutting implements.

There is the compulsory bag of pre-Victorian grass seed, out-of date ant powder, and solidified wood stain usually with a four-inch brush concreted into its mass.

In the corners, enormous cobwebs festoon every item that has been unused for a period of more than 24 hrs.

Arachnoids guard every square inch of worktop and roof space as the keeper pores over the workings of a cylinder head and a lukewarm cup of tea.